Understanding Force

Understanding Force

An account of some aspects of teaching the idea of
force in school, college and university courses in
engineering, mathematics and science

J. W. Warren, M.Sc., Ph.D.,
Senior Lecturer, Physics Dept.
Brunel University, London

John Murray, 50 Albemarle Street, London

Printed in Great Britain by Martins Printing Works Ltd

0 7195 3564 6

Contents

Preface

Force is fundamental to the study of engineering, science and applied mathematics. It has long been regarded as a simple concept, being less abstract than for example energy, and insufficient consideration has been given to ensuring that it is taught correctly. Consequently a large number of wrong or otherwise misleading ideas on the subject have come to be accepted and are widely taught in schools and in colleges and universities.

In this monograph an attempt has been made to expose some of the difficulties that students experience because of their wrong or imprecise ideas about force. The first three chapters summarise the principles and some of the inherent difficulties of the concept. Chapter 4 discusses some special forces and problems, the treatment of which often contributes to misunderstanding. Chapter 5 reports tests upon university entrants which indicate the seriousness of the errors and confusion that arise in the application of elementary mechanics to commonplace phenomena. The final chapter considers some relevant principles of pedagogy.

Figures 1, 14 and 15 originally appeared in articles in *Physics Education*.

1
Kinematics

Velocity and acceleration

The scientific study of motion is based on observations of position and time. The distance of a given point from another (reference) point is called its displacement. Displacement is a vector quantity, that is it has both magnitude and direction (see appendix 1).

Any number of vectors can be added according to the polygon law. This idea is probably best approached by considering the resultant of a number of successive displacements of a body. Thus we can consider the displacement of a traveller from his starting point and contrast this with the distance travelled. Such a discussion can illustrate the important idea that the average value of a vector quantity is zero over a cycle of changes.

The change of displacement of a point divided by the time taken is defined as the average velocity over this period of time. Instantaneous velocity is the limiting value for an infinitesimal time interval, that is, it is the rate of change of displacement.

There is almost universal agreement amongst teachers and authors that the name *velocity* should be given to this vector, and that *speed* should be used for the rate of change of distance travelled. Consequently a very large proportion of students will classify velocity and speed correctly in tests. Unfortunately the nature of the distinction is not always clearly understood, nor is the terminology consistently used. Displacement is very rarely discussed in elementary work, and velocity is usually just described as speed in a particular direction. (One elementary book explains that a train travelling on a straight track has speed whereas one on a curved track has velocity!) Very often the word 'velocity' is used where 'speed' would be more accurate, as, for example, in references to the 'velocity' of light or sound, or the muzzle 'velocity' of a gun. In innumerable problems numerical values are given for 'velocities' without any reference to direction. It cannot be expected, in the circumstances, that students will attach any real importance to a distinction that is made when the subject is first introduced and then ignored.

The change of velocity divided by the time taken is the average acceleration; taken to the limit, this gives instantaneous acceleration as the rate of change of velocity. Acceleration is a vector with the same direction as the change of velocity. In non-scientific use the word acceleration means rate of increase of speed; misunderstandings can therefore arise from confusion between the scientific and the common meanings. Such confusion is sometimes caused by the incorrect definition of acceleration in terms of *increase* of velocity, and by the invalid use of the separate term *deceleration* to mean certain cases of acceleration.

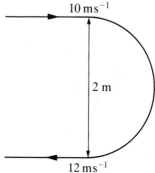

Figure 1 Diagram from a tutorial test. The student is asked to calculate the average velocity and acceleration for the semicircular path.

The following test has been employed to discover how well these concepts are understood by students. Students are first asked to identify the vectors in a list of quantities that includes speed, velocity and acceleration. Then figure 1 is given with this problem:

> A particle moves in the path shown, the speed increasing uniformly with time in the semicircular section, from 10 ms^{-1} to 12 ms^{-1}. For this section of the path calculate the averages of (a) the velocity, (b) the acceleration. (Assume $\pi = 22/7$)

The average speed is 11 ms^{-1}; hence the time taken for the semicircular path is (2/7)s. The average velocity is the displacement divided by the time, that is, 7 ms^{-1} straight downwards in the diagram. The change in velocity is 22 ms^{-1} to the left; hence the average acceleration is 77 ms^{-2} to the left.

Correct answers to these questions are practically never obtained. Almost all students give the average speed for the average velocity, although they have distinguished speed from velocity in the first part of the question. The question about acceleration is usually left unanswered. To anyone unfamiliar with the basic principles outlined above, this may appear to be a trick question; but, in fact, the answers should be immediately obvious to anyone who understands what is meant by velocity and acceleration (i.e. that each is the change of a *vector* divided by time taken).

Signs

A scalar has a sign and a magnitude—for example a mass of ten kilograms, a potential energy of minus five joules or the date 55 B.C. A vector has magnitude, which is inherently positive, and direction. The components of a vector in a rectangular Cartesian coordinate system can have positive or negative signs, and when we limit our study to one dimension we are, in effect, taking one Cartesian component. Much elementary work in mechanics is necessarily done in one dimension only; hence the existence of both positive and negative values for a quantity is sometimes wrongly regarded as implying that it is a vector. This is probably one reason why some scalars, such as potential energy, are often mistakenly thought to be vectors.

For work in one dimension a direction must be taken as positive for all vectors. Thus velocity, acceleration and force are positive if they are in the direction of positive displacement. Much confusion is caused by treating acceleration inconsistently. Many writers say that acceleration is negative, or call it deceleration, when a body is slowing down. The nature of the confusion can be illustrated by considering the simple periodic motion described by the equation

$$x = a \sin \omega t.$$

In the first quarter of a cycle the displacement and velocity are both positive. In S.P.M. the acceleration is always opposite in direction to the displacement, so in this quarter the acceleration is negative. As the acceleration is opposite to the velocity the body is slowing down.

During the next quarter cycle the displacement is still positive and the acceleration is negative. The velocity is negative and the body is increasing its speed.

In the third quarter, displacement is negative and acceleration positive. The velocity is negative and its *magnitude* is decreasing.

In the fourth quarter cycle displacement is negative and acceleration is positive. The velocity is now positive and increasing.

Time	Displacement	Velocity	Acceleration	Speed
0–$\frac{T}{4}$	+	+	−	Decreasing
$\frac{T}{4}$–$\frac{T}{2}$	+	−	−	Increasing
$\frac{T}{2}$–$\frac{3T}{4}$	−	−	+	Decreasing
$\frac{3T}{4}$–T	−	+	+	Increasing

Signs of vectors in simple periodic motion

These signs, of course, arise inevitably if we use the equation and obtain velocity and acceleration by differentiating once and twice respectively with respect to time. Clearly, if one calls a decreasing speed a negative acceleration, the sign will be inconsistent in the second and third quarters (see table on previous page).

The two points in the cycle when the body is instantaneously at rest are particularly interesting. At the first of these, when the time is exactly one quarter period ($t = T/4$), the speed is zero and the acceleration has maximum magnitude and is negative. At $t = 3T/4$ the speed is again zero, whilst the acceleration again has maximum magnitude and is positive. The idea that a body can be instantaneously at rest and yet be accelerated is very generally unfamiliar to students. It is, of course, necessary to recognise this fact in order to understand how anything can begin to move from rest, or how a ball or gas molecule can recoil from a wall.

Difficulties caused by the incorrect use of the negative sign to imply that speed is decreasing arise similarly when the motion of a body thrown upwards or a head-on collision of vehicles is being considered.

Uniform circular motion

In two or three dimensional space, the rate of change of a vector does not necessarily take place in the same line as the vector itself. It is essential to recognise the general meaning of acceleration as a rate of change, *not* a rate of increase. Students who are taught to regard acceleration as a rate of increase of speed, and to use negative acceleration or deceleration for a rate of decrease, find it very difficult to accept that a body is accelerating when its direction changes at constant speed. This is a serious problem because of the great importance of uniform circular motion.

Some of the published analyses of this phenomenon might well be expected to increase the difficulty. In some cases the velocity of an orbiting body is said to be constant, and then the rate of change is calculated to be v^2/r! Sometimes the acceleration is said to be constant, although this also is continuously changing direction. Very occasionally the argument is developed back-to-front: an experiment is described for measuring a centripetal force and the fact of acceleration is deduced from the existence of a force.

Perhaps much of the difficulty arises from the usual practice of starting the argument half way through: the difficult idea that acceleration is a vector is derived from the change of velocity, but the velocity is rarely derived from the change of displacement. Let us follow an approach from first principles.

Consider the displacement (from the centre) of a point moving with uniform angular velocity of magnitude ω in a circle of radius r, as shown in figure 2(a).

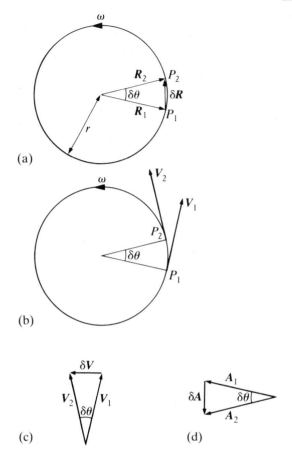

Figure 2 Vector diagrams used in deriving the instantaneous values of velocity, acceleration and rate of change of acceleration in uniform circular motion.

When the point is at P_1 its displacement from the centre is the vector R_1, and when it is at P_2 its displacement is R_2. These displacements each have the same *magnitude r* but they are unequal since their directions differ.

If the angle between R_1 and R_2 is $\delta\theta$, we have $\delta\theta/\delta t = \omega$. The difference δR between R_2 and R_1 is determined by finding the vector that must be added to R_1 to obtain R_2, as shown in figure 2(a). The average velocity from P_1 to P_2 is then $\delta R/\delta t$. This has a magnitude of approximately $r\ \delta\theta / \delta t$, and direction from P_1 to P_2. Taking the limit as δt tends to zero we find that the instantaneous velocity at P_1 is the vector V_1, tangential to the circle at P_1, with magnitude $r(d\theta/dt) = r\omega$.

5

1 Kinematics

If the derivation of the velocity is understood, the derivation of the acceleration follows naturally. Considering figure 2(b) we have to find the difference of V_2 minus V_1. Using the vector diagram in figure 2(c) and proceeding to the limit, we see that the acceleration at P_1 is a vector directed radially inwards, with magnitude $r\omega^2$.

The change of acceleration is found by using the vector diagram in figure 2(d). This shows that the rate of change of acceleration at P_1 is a vector of magnitude $r\omega^3$ opposite in direction to the velocity. This latter calculation should help to emphasize the vector nature of acceleration.

Newton's Laws of Motion

First law

We can state the law in the form: *Unless there is a resultant external force acting upon it, any body* moves with constant speed in a straight line.* Alternatively, we can state that the velocity remains constant, provided the meaning of velocity has been clearly distinguished from that of speed.

It must be noted that the laws of motion make no distinction in principle between different states of uniform rectilinear motion. Thus a body remaining at rest is a special case of no more or less significance than, for example, a body moving in a defined direction at a speed of 137 m s^{-1}. An invalid distinction is sometimes implied by incorrectly defining statics as the study of bodies at rest, and dynamics as the study of bodies in motion. Similarly equilibrium is sometimes wrongly identified with rest.

The first law (which also holds in special relativity physics) defines a system of mechanics. At a deeper level of enquiry there are major problems in formulating such a law. How, in fact, can we decide whether or not a body is moving with constant velocity? We require some framework (other than a blackboard) to define speed and direction. Newton took 'the sphere of the fixed stars' as providing such a framework and we shall do the same. Questions concerning the validity of such a procedure and the existence of any mechanism by which it may be supposed that the law is caused to operate are beyond the scope of this work. It is sufficient to postulate that physical laws can be considered from the ideal standpoint of an imaginary 'inertial observer' who finds that Newton's first law is true as far as his measurements are concerned.

Conceptual difficulties of the first law

At an elementary level the difficulty of understanding Newton's first law does not arise from such advanced questions as the nature of

---

* Strictly the law applies to particles. Extension of the first two laws to extended bodies (by applying them to the motion of the centre of mass) requires the consideration of internal interactions, which involves application of the third law.

absolute space. The problem is that the abstract concepts found necessary for the consistent description of phenomena are in conflict with ordinary non-scientific interpretation of commonplace experience. Our ideas of force and motion originate from bodily sensations, and we naturally make a fundamental distinction between being at rest and being in motion. We know that we must make an effort to keep moving with respect to our immediate surroundings and therefore, deep down in our minds, we are convinced that force is needed to *cause* motion and that motion occurs in the direction of that force. Physicists make the quite different assumption that forces are needed only to *change* motion—an idea that is repugnant to 'common sense'.

The tests on university students described in chapter 5 reveal some of the ways in which non-acceptance of the first law influences the way that students interpret phenomena. The extent to which pre-scientific concepts of force and motion are held, even by honours graduates, is shown by an examination of textbooks. Discussions of Brownian motion sometimes imply, or even explicitly state, that the instantaneous motion of particles is in the direction of the resultant force. Students are taught that the path of a free charge is an electric line of force (during demonstrations of apparatus showing electron beams graduates have asked 'why do not the electrons follow the lines of force?'). Accounts of Fleming's left-hand rule often state correctly in the text that the thumb indicates the force, whilst in the diagram the thumb is labelled 'motion'. This error probably originated partly from the use of a clumsy mnemonic which is based on the fact that 'm' appears in both 'motion' and 'thumb'. If a mnemonic is thought necessary it would be far better to propose that students remember that 'thumb' represents 'thrust'.

Force is sometimes defined as that which *causes* motion; The definition of work often begins with a phrase such as 'when a force moves a body . . .'; bodies are said to 'travel with great force', or to be 'kept moving by their own momentum'. A consideration of these and many similar expressions in books suggests that the authors unconsciously reject the fundamental concept of the first law of motion, which is clearly a most difficult idea. In education it must never be forgotten that one can with all sincerity subscribe to a doctrine and yet not really believe it.

Statement of the second law

The rate of change of momentum of a body is proportional to the resultant impressed force and takes place in the direction of this force. By suitable choice of units we can replace the proportionality with an equality, and write

$$\text{force} = \frac{\mathrm{d}}{\mathrm{d}t}(mv) \tag{1}$$

For a body of constant mass

$$\text{force} = m\,\frac{\mathrm{d}v}{\mathrm{d}t} = \text{mass} \times \text{acceleration} \tag{2}$$

For most purposes equation (2) is sufficiently accurate, but it is advantageous to start from the general form of equation (1). This leads immediately to the idea of impulse and, combined with the third law, gives conservation of momentum. It is also necessary for application to problems involving bodies of variable mass, such as rockets, and it later permits easy application of the idea of force in special relativity mechanics.

It is sometimes argued that the first law is just the special case of the second law when the force is zero. However, when one considers the great intellectual difficulty in mastering these ideas, it does appear that it is necessary to assert clearly the basic qualitative concept of force as something that *changes* motion, before considering the quantitative second law.

We may also ask here whether we are discussing natural laws, axioms or definitions. The doubt goes back to Newton, who wrote of 'axioms or laws of motion' (*axiomata sive leges motus*). It may be impossible for us to resolve this problem fully, but it should be noted that the second law does appear to imply a relationship between an observed effect and its supposed cause (the force), and that such a relationship, if it can be applied consistently, amounts to what is usually called a law.

Conceptual difficulties of the second law

In elementary work there are inevitably those difficulties always found in understanding quantitative relationships involving proportionalities. To overcome these, many experiments, demonstrations and numerical examples are given to illustrate uniformly accelerated rectilinear motion. The object is worthy, but one possible effect is to associate motion in the pupils' minds with a force in the direction of movement, thereby perhaps increasing the innate difficulty of appreciating the first law.

At a rather higher level, the student is usually troubled far more by the physics than by the mathematics of the subject. He is often not certain what forces are acting, by what mechanism they act, or where they act. When questioned about commonplace phenomena, he is

9

likely to confuse forces acting on different bodies and to introduce several non-existent forces.

Confusion between forces acting on different bodies often arises from a misunderstanding of the third law, or from ambiguity in the meaning of weight, as discussed later. To avoid such confusion one can usefully draw two or more diagrams to represent any interaction, each showing the forces acting on a particular body. Alternatively one can use distinct symbols, such as arrows of different colour.

There is much vagueness about how and where forces act on a body. Forces of all types are commonly represented as if they acted through the centre of gravity. Most university freshmen tested by the author suppose that a car engine applies a force, in some undefined way, directly to the vehicle, and they do not appreciate that it causes a frictional force to be exerted *by the ground* on the rear wheels. This is, perhaps, partly because they are taught that 'friction always opposes motion'. In teaching circular motion one may refer to the centripetal force. Too often instead of its being said that, say, the gravitational force *is* the centripetal force, it is said that it is *equal to* the centripetal force. Thus the student comes to imagine that there are two different but equal inwardly acting forces.

The idea of a resultant force causes many worries. Evidently some students think of the resultant as just another force, and many diagrams in textbooks represent it as if it were so. This could be avoided by using different symbols for resultants from those used for components, such as dashed lines to contrast with full lines, or different colours. Sometimes the name 'accelerating force' is given to the resultant and sometimes to one of the component applied forces.

All these difficulties could be avoided by precise descriptions of phenomena and the use of clear diagrams.

Statement of the third law

Forces result from the interactions of bodies. The force exerted by body A *upon body* B *is equal in magnitude, opposite in direction and in the same straight line as the force exerted by* B *upon* A.

For general application we must extend the idea of a body to include radiation, for example in the Compton scattering of a photon by an electron. Such cases often go beyond the scope of Newtonian physics.

By combining the second and third laws we can deduce the law of conservation of momentum. It is interesting to note that the third law does not apply exactly in all circumstances in special relativity mechanics, although the transformation of time is such that momentum conservation still holds.

The application of the third law to the interactions of the parts of an extended body enables us to use the first two laws in such cases by considering the motion of the centre of mass, it also makes possible the formulation of such concepts as moment of inertia.

Conceptual difficulties of the third law

This law is widely misunderstood because of the most unfortunate custom of expressing it in one of the epigrammatic forms, 'to every action there is an equal and opposite reaction' or 'every action is opposed by an equal reaction'. These statements are derived from the latin of the *Principia*. No doubt Newton was influenced by the contemporary tradition of classical learning that expected scholars to coin epigrams, but he did complete his statement by saying precisely what he meant. For generations the epigram has been much better known

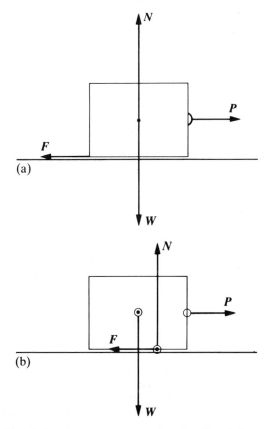

Figure 3   (a) A very common misrepresentation of the system of forces supposed to produce equilibrium when friction acts in the surfaces between a block and bench. (b) Correct representation.

than the explanation. It would be very much better to state the meaning of the law and omit the slogan.

The use of the terms 'action' and 'reaction' implies a sequence in time and the relation of cause and effect, whereas the forces referred to in Newton's third law both arise simultaneously from the same interaction and are of the same nature. The second form of the epigram is even worse than the first because the word 'opposed' suggests that the two forces must be acting on the same body. Hence some students think the law refers only to equilibrium. Perhaps it should be explained that 'opposed' formerly meant facing in opposite directions and did not necessarily imply conflict. One had an opponent not only in a duel, but also in a dance or in an intimate conversation.

One very common use of the term 'reaction' occurs in the discussion of friction. The standard diagram is that shown in Figure 3(a). The gravitational force on the block, usually called weight, is marked W. The intermolecular force of repulsion exerted by the bench on the block is called the 'normal reaction' (N) and is shown acting through the centre of gravity (indeed it is often shown as if it were applied here). Naturally students think of N as the 'reaction' to W in the sense of the third law. It is quite possible that those who draw such diagrams think so too, and for this reason draw N acting through the centre of gravity. Obviously, for the block to be in equilibrium, the repulsion must act to the right of the centre of gravity, as shown in Figure 3(b), where the effective points of application of the forces are indicated by the circles at the tails of the arrows.

The frequent use of the word 'reaction' in this and similar contexts, combined with the epigrammatic statement of the third law, leads to the belief that when a body interacts with the ground the upthrust is necessarily equal in magnitude to the gravitational force.

Confusion between pairs of forces acting on different bodies (according to the third law) and pairs of forces acting on a single body that is in equilibrium (according to the first law) is sometimes explicitly taught. Thus when one pushes a table the force of friction exerted by the ground on the table preventing acceleration is wrongly called the reaction to the force exerted by the hand. If, instead, there is negligible friction, the consequent rate of change of momentum (or minus this) is occasionally, very misleadingly, called the 'inertial reaction' (or 'kinetic reation'). A very striking example of this kind of erroneous statement of the third law is given in the following extract from an engineering textbook: 'If a body is stationary or moving with constant velocity then any applied force must have an equal and opposite force.' This is called the 'reaction force law'. In the subsequent development the word 'reaction' is usually applied to a force acting on the same body as the first force considered, but sometimes it is applied to a force acting on another body! (See p. 57.)

3
Imaginary Forces

Real and imaginary forces

The Newtonian system of mechanics can be developed fully in terms of real forces. By 'real' we mean forces which arise from definable interactions between bodies subject to recognisable laws, and such that the various conservation laws of mechanics (energy, momentum, angular momentum) are applicable. Sometimes, however, it is thought desirable to introduce certain imaginary forces into an analysis. These 'forces' are distinct from real ones in that there is no conceivable interaction between the bodies giving rise to them; they are subject to no laws other than somewhat arbitrary mathematical rules, and they fail to maintain one or more of the conservation laws.

It must be emphasised that although the use of imaginary forces may sometimes be convenient it is not necessary.

There are two commonly used types of imaginary force, which unfortunately have the very similar names *inertial forces* and *inertia forces*. Their character and use are very different, yet in certain cases they may appear so alike as to be very easily confused.

Inertial forces are particularly associated with Coriolis (1792–1843), and inertia forces with d'Alembert (1717–83).

Inertial forces

As has been stated previously (p. 7), Newton's laws of motion are found to be true by a hypothetical 'inertial observer'. Any observer who is accelerated with respect to the inertial observer will find that Newton's laws are not applicable in his system. For example, if a body is not under the action of any external force, the inertial observer will find that its velocity is constant, whilst the non-inertial observer will find that the body is accelerated with respect to himself.

The non-inertial observer may adopt any one of several alternative viewpoints. He may decide that his own system of reference is less satisfactory than that of the inertial observer, in which case he will correct all his readings accordingly. This is essentially the decision made by Copernicus and all the astronomers since his time who have described the solar system from the heliocentric viewpoint instead of directly from the viewpoint of the observatory. Alternatively he may decide to adopt an egocentric analysis in which he regards himself as unaccelerated. In this case, he may either use only real forces and abandon Newton's laws, or he may retain the first two laws at the expense of introducing imaginary 'inertial' forces acting on himself and every other body within the system studied.

The use of inertial forces can be illustrated by considering the motion of a shot fired due northwards from a gun in the northern hemisphere. An observer who is not sharing in the rotation of the earth may be regarded as an inertial observer (there is, of course, the question of the orbital motion around the sun and other larger scale astronomical phenomena, but we shall not follow these matters). This observer has no difficulty in understanding why the shot falls to the east of the line of longitude through the gun. Angular momentum must be conserved, so as the shot moves nearer to the axis of the earth it acquires a higher angular velocity and is displaced with respect to the ground in the direction of rotation. It is, however, very reasonable to try to consider the problem from the point of view of the gunner, who is not an inertial observer. His analysis will introduce *inter alia* a fictitious Coriolis force acting on the shot, deflecting it eastwards. Many problems concerned with movements of the atmosphere and the oceans are treated in this way.

A useful elementary discussion of inertial forces is given by Elton (1971), although it attributes a degree of reality to the forces which is not in accordance with the interpretation given here.

Inertia forces

There is an exposition of the laws of mechanics usually attributed to d'Alembert, although it owes much to several other workers. The formulation can be expressed in a number of ways and there are many very different statements of 'd'Alembert's principle'. A historical and critical survey is given by Ernst Mach in his famous book *The Science of Mechanics* (Mach 1919).

d'Alembert considered a system of interacting bodies. Forces are applied to these bodies by external agents, and also forces are exerted by the bodies on each other through various 'constraints'. Each body is thus acted upon by a resultant 'effective' force that causes acceleration according to Newton's second law. In some treatments it is found convenient to imagine that each body is also subject to a fictitious 'inertia force', or 'reversed effective force', equal and opposite to the resultant of the real forces. In this way problems in dynamics are converted into pseudo-equilibrium problems which can be treated by the methods of statics. The logic of this procedure is obscure since, although it involves the negation of Newton's laws, these laws are nevertheless implicit in certain stages of the argument.

The methods of d'Alembert have no advantage in any of the problems normally considered in elementary work, and it is therefore unnecessary for us to consider them in detail. What *is* relevant is that the use of the imaginary inertia force has led to the frequent invocation of such forces, often out of context, and often without consideration of their nature. Some writers even believe that the supposed inertia force on a body is related to the real resultant force by Newton's third law. By this argument it appears that, quite literally, no body in the universe could ever be acted upon by any resultant force.

Evidently the use of imaginary forces has a strong appeal for some workers. This is demonstrated by the approach of one very able author (Den Hartog 1948) who, unlike most writers, quotes (in translation) d'Alembert's original paper. He explains the archaic expressions of the original in modern terms and calls the resultant real forces on the bodies 'the negative inertia forces'. Clearly, in this passage, d'Alembert only found it necessary to use real forces. It has become so common to introduce totally imaginary negatives to the real forces that a modern author finds it quite natural to call the real forces negative inertia ones!

Inertia and inertial forces compared

The different types of imaginary force can be compared by considering the simple, if rather artificial, example illustrated in figure 4. Two blocks with masses m_1 and m_2 are joined by a light string which passes over a frictionless and inertialess pulley. m_1 slides without friction on the horizontal surface.

In (a) we see the system as described by Newton. Each of the bodies is subject to a force of magnitude F resulting from the tension in the string. They have accelerations of equal magnitude a in the directions shown. A simple analysis using Newton's second law tells us that a equals $m_2 g$ divided by $(m_1 + m_2)$. The observer is inertial and does not need to imagine any fictitious force.

In (b) we see the system as described by Coriolis. The observer is accelerated with respect to Newton's inertial system so that he is unaccelerated with respect to the block m_1. He can measure the real force F acting on m_1. In order to retain Newton's first and second laws he introduces an imaginary inertial force I_1 of magnitude $m_1 a$ acting on m_1, in a direction opposite to the acceleration as seen by Newton. According to this observer the mass m_2 has acceleration of magnitude $\sqrt{2}a$ in the direction shown. To retain Newton's second law he imagines an inertial force I_2 of magnitude $m_2 a$ directed as illustrated.

It is apparent that the 'forces' I_1 and I_2 do not obey Newton's third law and that the conservation laws do not apply.

Coriolis could, of course, have chosen to travel with m_2 with similar consequences.

3 Imaginary Forces

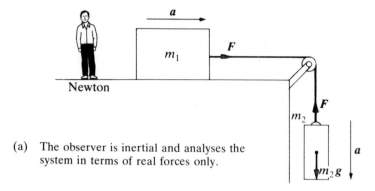

(a) The observer is inertial and analyses the system in terms of real forces only.

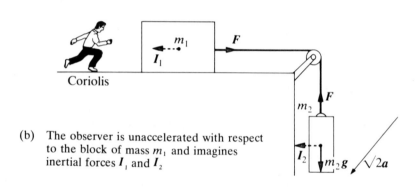

(b) The observer is unaccelerated with respect to the block of mass m_1 and imagines inertial forces I_1 and I_2

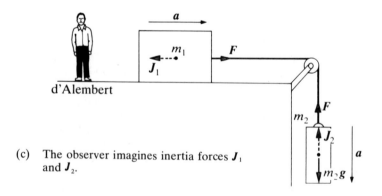

(c) The observer imagines inertia forces J_1 and J_2.

Figure 4 A simple hypothetical system seen from the viewpoint of (a) Newton, (b) Coriolis, (c) a follower of d'Alembert.

16

In (c) we see the system as described by a disciple of d'Alembert. Fictitious inertia forces J_1 and J_2 with magnitudes of m_1a and m_2a respectively, are supposed to act on the masses m_1 and m_2 in directions opposite to their observed accelerations. In this case none of Newton's laws of motion is applicable and the conservation laws do not hold.

It is interesting to note that the inertial force I_1 and the inertia force J_1 are equal in magnitude and direction, and are supposed to act in the same place. Thus in some circumstances these fundamentally different approaches are likely to be confused. In particular, some writers limit their application of d'Alembert's principle to rigid bodies, and in such cases one can postulate non-inertial observers who would imagine inertial forces equivalent to other observers' inertia forces. This equivalence does not apply to all kinds of constraint.

Imaginary forces and circular motion

Consider a body of mass m in uniform circular motion with speed v in a circle of radius r. If the centre is unaccelerated as seen by an inertial observer the latter can analyse the system simply in Newtonian terms, since there is necessarily a real resultant (centripetal) force of magnitude mv^2/r acting on the body. This approach is so simple that it is incomprehensible that students in elementary courses should ever be expected to use other, potentially confusing, approaches.

To adopt the viewpoint of Coriolis the observer must be rotating with respect to the fixed stars. To him the mass m appears to be unaccelerated, and he imagines a 'force' equal in magnitude and opposite in direction to the observed real force in order to annul it. He might call this a 'centrifugal' force, but as, in his system, there is no question of m having any motion related to a centre the terms centripetal and centrifugal are not properly relevant. It is sometimes said that the viewpoint of the non-inertial observer is as valid as is that of the inertial observer in describing such a system. This is true provided we do genuinely use the non-inertial observer's description of events. What is usually done is to state that a body is in uniform circular motion—which is the inertial observer's description—and then to introduce the inertial force. Now if we are to use an inertial force we must be consistent and describe the body as being at rest with the remainder of the observable universe moving around a suitable point. This implies that there are spectacular imaginary forces acting on other bodies in the universe, which are normally forgotten.

It is often unclear, in such cases, whether the (tacitly) assumed non-inertial observer is conceived of as being attached to the orbiting body (e.g. as a passenger is attached to a vehicle) or as independently rotating. Sometimes, as an argument for the 'reality' of inertial forces, it is argued that a passenger in a vehicle 'feels' a force throwing him

17

outwards. This is clearly an essentially psychological interpretation, based on our unconscious attempts to relate ourselves to our immediate surroundings, which we regard as static. For such arguments the observer must be attached to (or constitute) the orbiting body.

Sometimes, instead, it is said that, if one breaks a link in the structure through which the centripetal force is applied, the body has an initial acceleration given by the 'centrifugal force'. This approach assumes a rotating observer who is not attached to the orbiting body. It is a very odd argument for the reality of the inertial force, since it only applies to an instant when the body is no longer in circular motion! The rotating observer would attribute the same apparent acceleration to any body which passed by in a suitable tangential path without ever having been involved in the rotation.

When the d'Alembert method is used, an inertia force may be imagined acting opposite to the real centripetal force. In this case we retain the viewpoint of an inertial observer but abandon Newton's laws of motion. Whatever advantages this might have in any other application, it is inconceivable that it can contribute anything but confusion to this particular problem.

Whether one uses an inertial or an inertia force there should be no doubt as to its purely imaginary nature, but sometimes there is supposed to be a real centrifugal force acting on an orbiting body. This could arise from a misunderstanding or misuse of Newton's third law.

One possibility is that the student has been taught correctly that, since there is a centripetal force on the orbiting body, there must, by the third law, be an equal and opposite force on another body, and he carelessly thinks that this force acts on the orbiting body itself. The common vagueness about which objects forces act upon could easily cause this mistake. Another possibility is that the third law has been learned in the 'action and reaction' form, and the student supposes that the 'reaction' acts upon the same body as the 'action'.

It should be noted that the true third-law partner to the centripetal force is not necessarily centrifugal in direction. For example, the earth exerts a gravitational force on the moon so, by the third law, the moon exerts a gravitational force on the earth. *Both* forces are directed towards the centre of mass about which the system rotates; that is *both* are centripetal.

Almost invariably when a centrifugal force is introduced into an elementary textbook there is confusion which could easily be avoided by omitting the concept. One interesting example occurs in an under-graduate level book which considers the circular motion of charges in electric and magnetic fields. In an electric field, it is said, 'the electric force is balanced by the centripetal force', whilst in a magnetic field 'the magnetic force is counterbalanced by the centrifugal force'.

It is remarkable that imaginary forces are very often introduced into accounts of circular motion in books that do not use the idea at all in other cases, for example linear motion or projectiles or elliptic orbits. Thus an imaginary force becomes a mystery uniquely related to one particular problem.

If the reader has a colleague who insists on teaching that there is a centrifugal force acting on a circulating body in uniform circular motion, he could ask the following questions.

Is the force real or imaginary?

If it is imaginary, is it an inertial or an inertia force?

Is the observer an inertial observer?

Which of Newton's laws of motion apply?

If Newton's third law applies, which force is the 'partner' to the centrifugal force?

Where in the body does the force act?

Are there any consequent forces acting on any other body?

Would there be a similar force acting on a body that is accelerating in a straight line?

It would be interesting to observe his reaction.

Special Problems

Weight

Weight is usually defined as the force of gravity acting on a body. Some authors use the word to mean the force that a supported body exerts on its support. More rarely it is used to mean the force exerted by the support. Sometimes the support is required to be at rest with respect to the surface of the earth, but at other times the support may be, for example, an accelerating lift. Sometimes weight is just equated to mg without any explicit statement about where it acts. There is here the additional difficulty that, as the earth is rotating, the acceleration to the surface of the earth, g, is not quite the same as the acceleration to the centre.

Very often weight is defined as the force of gravity on a body, but then it is said that the weight 'acts downwards on the support'; thus there is confusion as to which body the force is acting on. The point of application of weight also wanders unpredictably between the centre of gravity and the surface of a body.

The use of 'weight' to mean the force exerted on a support is rarely explicit now, but it was probably more common in the past. Perhaps one reason why the upthrust on the block of figure 3(a) is so often called the 'reaction' is that it was originally so called by authors for whom 'weight' meant the force exerted on the bench. In that case the 'weight' would, in fact, be a downward force equal and opposite to the upthrust of figure 3(b) and in the same straight line. 'Weight' with this meaning would be related to upthrust by the third law; it would not, however, act through the centre of gravity.

The author has found that there is so much vagueness and confusion about the meaning of weight that he very rarely uses the term in lectures, but instead specifies precisely which force he means.

When one is unsupported, as in an orbiting space vehicle (i.e. one in free-fall), one is said to be 'weightless'. This term is obviously meaningful if by 'weight' one means the force exerted on a support. However, young people of the generation that has grown up in a world where references to weightlessness are commonplace have mostly been taught that weight is the force of gravity on a body. Thus they naturally assume that an astronaut is weightless because he is beyond the effective range of the earth's field. Most of the university entrants we have tested estimated that the value of gravity at the typical height of an artificial satellite (200 km above the ground) must be less than one per cent of the ground level value. Clearly the inverse square law means little to them; nor have they considered why the satellite follows a curved path. Other students appreciate that gravity still has a substantial value at the height of the satellite, but believe it to be cancelled by 'centrifugal force'. It may be worth observing that weightlessness does not depend on the shape of the orbit, since most of the students we have tested suppose that it only occurs during circular motion.

The idea of weightlessness is further confused by certain errors in early works of science fiction. In a well known story of a journey to the moon (Verne 1865) the travellers are wrongly supposed to have normal terrestrial experience of weight throughout the flight except when passing through a small region where the gravitational fields of the earth and moon cancel each other (the field of the sun is forgotten!).

The physiological effects attributed to 'weight' deserve some consideration. Organisms living on the earth are subjected to a gravitational field acting throughout their volumes. They are supported by forces applied to their surfaces, which are either distributed over a large area as in aquatic plants and animals, or localised as in trees and horses. When opposing forces are applied to different parts of a structure it is said to be in a state of stress. All living things are exposed to such stress and their structure and metabolism are affected by it. The state of stress in a large non-aquatic animal such as man is considerable; hence removal of the support causes great disturbance to his physiology. Even a tiny seed is stressed by the non-coincident opposing forces of gravity and the upthrust of soil, which is why the root is stimulated to grow downwards when the seed germinates.

Similar states of stress can be produced by accelerating organisms with forces applied to their surfaces. For example, if a seed is kept in soil on a rotating support, its root will grow in a direction opposite to that of the supporting force, which is no longer vertical. A man in an aircraft undergoing a large acceleration may suffer severe effects from the increased stress to which he is subjected. This is not because he is accelerated but because the acceleration is caused by a non-uniformly applied force. If he were in free fall near Jupiter he would have a very large acceleration, but would be weightless.

In a space station 'artificial gravity' could be produced by acceleration to simulate roughly the stresses we experience on earth, but we must be careful not to interpret too literally the equivalence of acceleration to a gravitational field. A space station is set into rotation about its axis (figure 5). The outer wall (the 'floor') exerts an inward force on the astronaut's feet which causes stresses throughout his body that have similar effects to those that he is adapted to on earth. He might

21

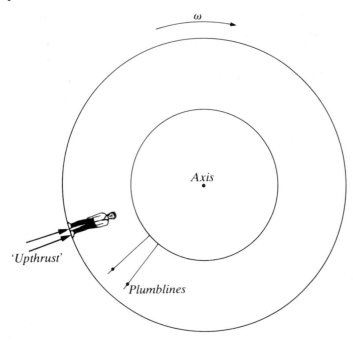

Figure 5 'Artificial gravity' in a rotating space station.

suppose that he is in a gravitational field directed radially outwards. He could however easily distinguish his situation from that on earth by performing simple mechanical tests, such as dropping objects, or suspending plumb-lines from different points. His 'field of force' becomes greater as his 'lines of force' become further apart.

Deformation

When studying elastic deformation we are usually concerned with bodies in equilibrium which are stressed by systems of opposing forces applied to different parts of the bodies.

The extension of a wire or a rod is caused by a tension arising from equal attractive forces acting at its ends. A tension, although measured in units of force, is clearly quite different from an applied resultant force. It is therefore misleading to state, as is so often done, that 'the wire is stretched by a force'. In some diagrams, the load on one end of a specimen is shown, but the force exerted by the clamp at the other end is omitted. The force exerted by the cord on the bob of a simple pendulum is often called 'the tension in the cord'. It might be thought that little harm could result from such looseness of expression, as there

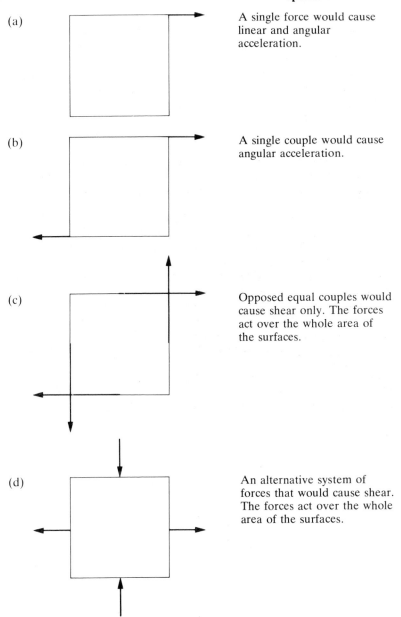

(a)   A single force would cause linear and angular acceleration.

(b)   A single couple would cause angular acceleration.

(c)   Opposed equal couples would cause shear only. The forces act over the whole area of the surfaces.

(d)   An alternative system of forces that would cause shear. The forces act over the whole area of the surfaces.

Figure 6   (a) and (b) are common incorrect illustrations of forces supposed to be responsible for shear stress; (c) and (d) are both correct, although they would result in different kinds of deformation.

appears, at first, to be little scope for misunderstanding; but that misunderstanding does in fact occur becomes apparent when these ideas are extended to surface tension (discussed in the next section) and even to a simple shear stress.

Common textbook misrepresentations of the system of forces causing shear are shown in diagrams (a) and (b) in figure 6. Both these systems would, in fact, cause angular acceleration and (a) would also cause translational acceleration. To produce the effect described in the definition of the shear (rigidity) modulus we need a pair of opposing couples as shown in figure 6(c).

The system of forces applied as pressures shown in 6(d) is sometimes said to be equivalent to the forces shown in 6(b), although it should be obvious that these two sets of forces would have totally different effects.

Although the forces of 6(c) and 6(d) cause different changes of shape, their effects are equivalent at the molecular level.

According to Newton's third law, when forces or couples are applied to a body, there are equal and opposite forces or couples acting on other bodies. It may be that some authors suppose that equilibrium is produced by the 'opposition' of the third law interactions, not understanding that forces acting on different bodies cannot be combined in this way. It is sometimes incorrectly said that the applied forces are 'opposed by internal forces', which does imply this interpretation. This may account in part for such misrepresentations as those shown in 6(a) and 6(b).

Other examples of similar absurdities are shown in figures 7 and 8. Figure 7 shows a common illustration of a single couple acting on a section of a bent beam. The external opposing couple needed to

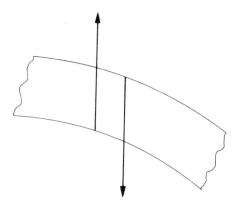

Figure 7 Common misrepresentation of the forces acting on a bent beam; the couple shown would, in fact, cause angular acceleration.

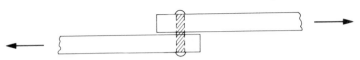

Figure 8 Incorrect diagram that is purported to show the shearing of a rivet. Two forces acting as shown would also cause angular acceleration.

prevent angular acceleration is omitted. Figure 8 purports to show the shearing of a rivet joining two bars of metal in tension. Since the forces illustrated do not act in the same line, the system as shown could not be in equilibrium; in practice the bars would bend.

Surface tension

There is a long-established tradition that one should teach the origin of surface tension in terms of intermolecular forces. It is strange that there is no similar tradition of explaining in molecular terms the ability of solids and liquids to resist both extension and compression (see appendix 2).

The published 'explanations' of surface tension contain such absurd errors of elementary mechanics that they must contribute significantly to the confusion that most students experience in this subject. They also reveal very clearly that this confusion is shared by the students' elders and betters!

The traditional argument is as follows: Molecules are said to attract each other with forces that decrease rapidly with increasing separation and the supposed effects of such forces are represented in a diagram such as figure 9. A molecule in the interior of a liquid is said to be attracted equally in all directions and therefore to remain in equilibrium, whereas a molecule in the surface is said to be attracted less on one side than on the other. Thus there is an inwardly directed resultant force acting on the surface molecules. Because of this, it is said, the surface molecules 'tend to move inwards', and the surface is therefore in tension.

It is incredible that such an analysis could ever have been published — that it is nonsense is (or should be) obvious. Yet not only has it been published, it has also been widely accepted as a serious scientific argument for a long time. We must examine the argument in detail.

The first point to notice is that it is usually assumed that only attractive forces exist between molecules. This creates the mystery of why matter does not just collapse inwards. In fact, matter is more difficult to compress than to extend. Also, how is it that molecules do not just pass through other matter without resistance, and that gases can be contained and exert pressure? The rarely asked question, 'what

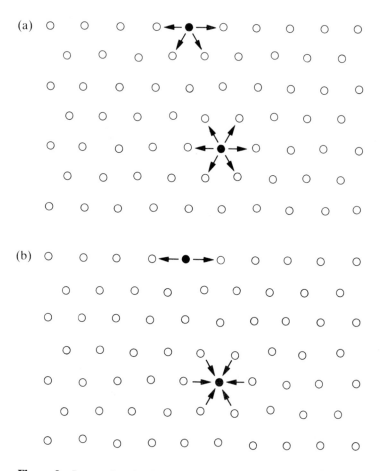

Figure 9 Intermolecular forces in a liquid are traditionally shown acting as in (a). This representation is incorrect because it implies that the surface of the liquid is accelerating inwards and that the interior is in tension. The correct representation is shown in (b); here the surface is in tension and the interior is in compression.

keeps particles apart?' is just as significant as the popular one 'what keeps them together?'

Secondly, it is assumed that a molecule will *stay in equilibrium* if pulled equally on each side. But the argument assumes that the forces are attractive and decreasing with distance. Hence, given the slightest displacement, a molecule will be subject to a resultant force *away* from the point of equilibrium, and the system will be completely unstable.

26

Thirdly, it is assumed that molecules in the interior of a liquid are *pulled* on each side. This describes a body in a state of tension. But in nearly all circumstances in which we are concerned with surface tension the bulk of the liquid is in a state of compression, usually because of atmospheric pressure.

Next, it is asserted that molecules in the surface are acted on by an inward force which 'tends to move' them. This, of course, is in conflict with the concept of force expressed by Newton's laws. If there were a resultant inward force on the surface molecules, the surface would accelerate inwards and matter as we know it could not exist.

Finally we must note the false assumption that a resultant force is the same thing as a tension.

This absurd 'explanation' continues to be taught despite criticism (e.g. Warren 1965) and even the doubts of its own advocates. In *Tribology* (Schools Council 1974), where a conventional presentation is given, the comment is made: 'It may seem strange that a force which originates as a net force directed into the liquid should give rise to a surface tension along the surface and perpendicular to the molecular resultant force'. This is a common difficulty for both students and teachers. They are troubled to explain why a force in one direction should produce a tension at right angles to it, yet they accept without question the preposterous supposition that there is a resultant force.

In a few textbooks the conventional treatment is given with the refinement that, as well as the supposed resultant attractive forces which are said to cause surface tension, there are also repulsive forces (usually caused 'reactions') which are said to give stability. The logic of this procedure is odd. Since it is admitted that both attractive and repulsive intermolecular forces exist, one would expect that the argument would be based on the resultant of all forces. If one is permitted to isolate the attractive forces and to deduce from them that the surface is in tension, one might equally consider just the repulsive forces and hence prove that the surface is in compression.

One other variant is worthy of notice. In this argument it is appreciated that the surface molecules are attracted when they oscillate further out than their equilibrium positions and repelled when they move in closer. (This basically sound description is rather marred by a molecule being compared to a ball bouncing perfectly elastically, for which the contrast between attractive and repulsive forces is more extreme; but this does not really affect the argument.) The assumption is then made that as the attractive forces act for a longer time we can still regard the surface molecules as being under resultant attractive forces. This ignores the fact that, although the shorter-range repulsive forces act for shorter times, they are so much larger than the attractive forces that the average force over a cycle of oscillation is zero.

4 Special Problems

Jets and recoil

Jets of liquids and gases are very frequently obtained by expelling the liquid or gas through a suitably designed nozzle, often with very high speed. To produce a high speed jet a force must be exerted on the fluid, hence, by the third law, an equal and opposite force must act on the driving mechanism.

As a simple example, consider the 'jet propelled' balloon shown in figure 10. If the speed of the air is to increase as if flows through the

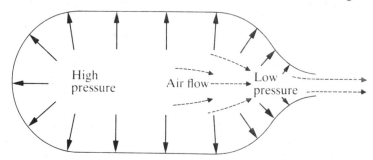

Figure 10 A 'jet-propelled' balloon. Compressed air exerts a greater force on the left-hand end than on the right-hand end. The effective propulsive force thus acts on the end remote from the nozzle. (The arrows represent forces applied to the balloon by the air.)

tapering nozzle there must be a pressure gradient within the nozzle such that the pressure is low where the speed is high, as stated in the well-known Bernoulli principle. Thus the magnitude of the total force exerted by the compressed air on the nozzle end of the balloon must be less than that applied at the opposite end. The balloon is propelled by a force equal and opposite to the force exerted on the expelled air.

It is widely believed and sometimes explicitly taught that, in such cases, the driving force acts on the nozzle, and the nozzle pushes the balloon, although it should be clear that there is no mechanism by which this could occur. In fact there must be a force on the nozzle in the direction of the jet, caused partly by friction, and partly by the resultant of the axial components of the forces exerted on the nozzle by air pressure. The nozzle is *pulled* by the balloon, it does not *push* it.

A standard exercise is to calculate the supposed backward force on the nozzle of a hose which is projecting a jet of water with a given speed and a given cross-section. As many of us have discovered, if a nozzle on a hose or tap becomes loose it will be blown off—not driven back more firmly into place as the 'theory' would suggest. Correct interpretation of such phenomena is obstructed by the other common experience of seeing the nozzle being pulled back by the hose. This is caused by forces exerted on the hose by water in bends. Such forces depend upon the curvature.

The existence of a backward force at a nozzle is sometimes assumed in descriptions of such devices as Hero's engine (figure 11). Actually the driving forces must act on the bends in the pipes.

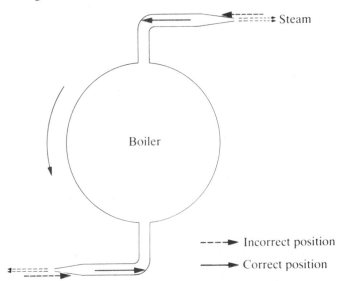

Steam

Boiler

----▶ Incorrect position

——▶ Correct position

Figure 11   Hero's steam engine. A backward force is often wrongly shown acting on the nozzles; it should be shown acting at the bends.

The propellant force acting on a vehicle from which fluid is being ejected, such as a rocket or jet engine, is often called a 'reaction', and such processes are called 'reaction propulsion'. It is remarkable that the same people who use the word 'reaction' for such forces will state Newton's third law in the form 'to every action there is an equal and opposite reaction'. Since, by their terminology, *every* force is necessarily a reaction, it is both illogical and confusing for them to take a particular case and distinguish it by this name. To propel any vehicle against dissipative friction or gravity, or to increase its speed, a force must be exerted on it by some outside body. Hence, by the third law, a force must be exerted by the vehicle on that other body. This is equally true for a motor car, a jet aircraft or one with a screw propeller, a rowing-boat, a screw or paddle driven ship, a sailing boat or a cart pulled by a horse.

Elasticity

For various purposes it is convenient, or indeed necessary, to consider problems in terms of ideally elastic materials and even to assume, in

29

effect, that elastic moduli are infinite. This would do no harm if it were not for the fact that such idealisations are often treated as if they were statements of objective fact. This can lead to serious misunderstanding.

Although the volume changes of gases with changing pressure are usually sufficiently large to be important in problems of fluid flow, those of liquids are usually infinitesimal. Hence it is usual to call liquids incompressible. Students sometimes believe this to be literally true and imagine that the bulk modulus is infinite.

A similar difficulty arises in the case of interactions of solid bodies, where it is imagined that infinite forces act over zero distances and that the entire body responds instantaneously. In fact, not all of the mass of a body responds instantaneously to a force applied to its surface, but instead a wave of disturbance is propagated through it at the speed of sound in the material. For example, if a gun that is rigidly attached to solid rock is fired, we do not have to consider the mass which recoils initially to be the whole mass of the earth. The effective mass is that of as much material as can be reached by waves travelling through the gun mounting and the rock during the time (of the order of milliseconds) during which the explosion occurs.

One important defect of elasticity is hysteresis, that is the dimensions of a body for a given stress during unloading often differ from the values during loading. Students are usually taught to disregard this fact, and are expected to average load and unload readings as if they were different measurements of the same thing. This phenomenon has important effects in rolling bodies such as wheels. Both the wheel and the ground beneath it are distorted as the wheel revolves, and imperfect elasticity, particularly hysteresis, leads to energy dissipation. This causes rolling friction, which is quite different from the friction that resists the sliding of one surface over another and is generally much smaller. Although it is a very common phenomenon, rolling friction is rarely mentioned other than in specialist advanced courses, and much confusion arises from attempts to interpret frictional resistance to vehicles or bodies rolling down slopes in terms of sliding friction.

Fluid pressure

It has been known since the time of Torricelli and Pascal that fluids exert forces on any surfaces in contact with them. In a purely static case the force will be perpendicular to the surface, whether we are concerned with a physical interface between the fluid and a solid or other fluid, or just with the force exerted by one part of a fluid on another. Such forces are nearly always repulsive, although, in some circumstances, liquids can be brought into tension. If the interaction over the surface can be regarded as uniform, the normal force divided by the area is called the *pressure* of the fluid. (Some engineers use the term *pressure intensity*.)

Few people have much difficulty in understanding that, for example, density (mass/volume) is not a mass, and that speed (distance/time) is not a distance, yet pressure (force/area) is apparently commonly thought to be a force. It seems that a force caused by a pressure is confused with the pressure itself. Thus we meet such ideas as 'pressure is a force acting in all directions', 'pressure is normal to the surface' and 'pressure is an omnidirectional vector'. Diagrams show arrows perpendicular to surfaces, labelled 'atmospheric pressure'. It should be made clear that pressure is not a force, but a condition in a fluid that causes forces to act normally to every surface. The force acting on any particular surface is a vector, but the pressure associated with it has no direction and is one of those quantities called pseudoscalars (see appendix 1).

A rather different misunderstanding is expressed by such statements as 'the pressure pushes the gas along the pipe'. Actually the driving force per unit volume is the *gradient* of the pressure (corrected for differences of level).

The concept of pressure can be extended without modification to solids only if we are concerned with uniform compression. The rigidity of solids generally causes very complex systems of stresses and strains. It may be advisable not to use the term pressure for a compressive stress in a solid unless the stress is being applied hydrostatically. We should also be very cautious about introducing or explaining pressure by discussing interactions of solids, such as the stresses that occur when shoes are thrust against the ground or a nail is driven into wood.

Tests on Students

We must consider how it is possible to determine whether or not a student understands a concept such as force. In an examination he may be asked to reproduce a piece of bookwork—for example, to state Newton's laws. An incorrect or incomplete answer may show that the laws are not understood, but a word-perfect answer may just be the product of memorisation without understanding. This does not mean that we should not ask questions on bookwork or expect essential ideas to be learned by heart; it does mean, however, that something further is required.

An examiner may ask for an example to illustrate the application of a law. Since it is likely that a student will have learned illustrative examples in the same way he learned the statements of the laws themselves, we have no assurance that he understands the example just because he can reproduce it. For instance, a popular example of Newton's third law of motion is rocket propulsion. Several writers of textbooks present this quite correctly, stating that just as the rocket exerts a force on the expelled gases so the gases exert an equal and opposite force on the rocket. Yet some of these same authors use the law wrongly in other applications. Evidently they have memorised or copied the example without understanding it.

It seems that a better way to investigate the understanding of principles is to ask the student to apply them to problems that he is unlikely to have learned a set answer to. This is quite easy to do in elementary mechanics, since the principles are so widely applicable. This chapter presents the results of posing such questions to groups of students, most of whom were freshmen in university courses in engineering, mathematics and science.

Application of Newton's laws

Several years ago the author set a question in a first-year university physics examination in which candidates were asked to state Newton's laws and to use them in a discussion of the mechanics of a small object such as a coin, that is (a) resting on a table, and (b) in flight after being thrown.

Various discussions of the mechanics were written, but not one contained any reference, explicit or implicit, to Newton's laws. The same question has been asked during oral discussions with some hundreds of first year physics students and applicants for entry into physics degree courses, who have been seen either individually or in small groups. These students invariably attempt to answer the question by talking about some irrelevant concept, such as energy. The advantage of the oral test is that it is eventually possible, although quite difficult, to persuade the young people that what is desired is a discussion in terms of Newton's laws. Provided they have some idea of what the laws are, the more able students can be guided—with considerable difficulty—along a path of reasoning such as the following. 'The coin on the table is at rest; hence, from the first law, we conclude that there is no resultant force on it.' (Complications such as the rotation of the earth are usually omitted.) 'The coin in flight is neither at rest nor in uniform motion in a straight line; hence we conclude that there is a resultant force acting on it.'

The extension of the discussion to the second law is then ordinarily rather more easy, although the flight of a coin is sometimes described roughly as follows: 'When it is going up it is decelerated; then at the top action and reaction are equal and opposite so it stops; then it accelerates downwards.' Usually, however, we can agree that it has constant acceleration throughout flight, and after some discussion the students realise that the second law implies that the force also must be constant.

With very few exceptions, the students are unable to apply the third law. Almost all of them assume that the coin remains at rest on the table because 'action and reaction are equal and opposite'. The idea that the law refers to forces acting on *different* bodies, and that they are applying it to forces on the *same* body, is usually incomprehensible. In the discussion of a coin in flight the third law is usually misapplied in one of a few ways: 'The reaction to the force of gravity is the force with which you threw it up.' 'The reaction is the force on the air.' 'The law does not apply because the coin is not in equilibrium.'

One essential idea that is almost always completely unfamiliar to the students is that the third law refers to interactions. They do not understand that, if a gravitational force is exerted on one body, the law requires that a *gravitational* force must act on *another* body.

The bouncing ball

This test has been given to new entrants into science and engineering courses, and to a smaller number of more advanced students of physics (principally graduates training to be teachers). The duplicated test paper includes figure 12 and the student is instructed to draw labelled arrows indicating the forces acting on the ball at points P and Q, and to estimate roughly the relative magnitude of these forces.

The answers are very varied, but some features are very often observed. Nearly everyone shows gravity at P, but some students omit

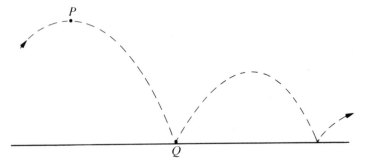

Figure 12   Diagram from a tutorial test. The student is asked to mark in the forces acting on the ball at points P and Q, and to indicate their probable relative magnitudes.

it at Q. At P there is often shown a force in the direction of motion and occasionally an upward force equal to gravity. An upward force at Q, usually called 'reaction', is shown in most cases. This force is commonly said to be equal to the weight of the ball. It should be obvious that this repulsive force must be relatively very large, but hardly any students appreciate this.

In tutorial discussions following these tests students express their conviction that the 'reaction' at Q must be equal in magnitude to the weight. When it is pointed out that a ball under zero resultant force would continue with constant speed in a straight path into the soil they are perplexed and usually have no idea how to resolve the difficulty.

Graduates from various universities being trained as science teachers do little better than undergraduate freshmen in this and similar tests.

The interpretation of students' answers to such tests is complicated by the frequent use of arrows that are marked as representing, or appear to represent, quantities which are not forces. These include vectors such as acceleration and momentum, and scalars such as kinetic energy and inertia to which the student is attributing direction. The addition of instructions not to mark in any quantities other than forces makes no difference to the results. Tutorial discussions suggest that some students regard all these quantities as essentially the same thing as forces.

The elliptic orbit

When certain textbooks were found to illustrate elliptic orbits with the more massive body at the centre instead of near a focus it was decided to find out whether students would detect the error. The deliberately incorrect diagram of figure 13 was duplicated and freshmen were asked to find the mistake and to mark in forces. About one third detected the error, one third said there was nothing wrong, and one third asserted that the orbit of any satellite must be a perfect circle. In discussions the latter students made it clear that, if they had heard of

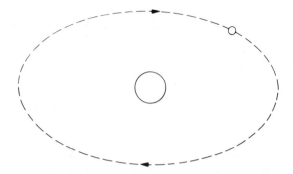

Figure 13   Diagram from a tutorial test, based upon incorrect representations of elliptic orbits in various textbooks. Students are asked to indicate the forces acting on the planet and its satellite, and to state what is wrong with the diagram.

elliptic orbits, they believed these to be caused by perturbations that are impossible in the absence of other bodies. This conviction, which is remarkably hard to dispel by argument, is shared by some graduates. This was a most interesting discovery since it had previously been completely unexpected. It suggests that a more extensive use of tests of this kind might reveal other common misunderstandings of which we should be made aware.

The 'forces' shown by students include the usual force in the direction of motion, centrifugal force, centripetal force (distinct from gravity), actions and reactions, and also quantities which are not forces. It is noticeable that the imaginary forces are often shown acting on the satellite but very rarely on the planet.

Although this is not a case of uniform circular motion, inward and outward forces are sometimes labelled mv^2/r.

The cornering car

This test has been used with several hundred university entrants. Results obtained in the first two years have been published in detail (Warren 1971a). The instructions are as follows.

A motor vehicle travels with uniform speed on level ground, turning to the right in a path of uniform curvature. There is no wind. Sketch a plan, showing

(a) an arrow marked **R** representing the resultant of all forces acting on the vehicle in the horizontal plane;

(b) an arrow marked F representing the resultant force of friction exerted by the ground on the vehicle;

(c) suitably labelled arrow(s) representing any other force or forces acting on the vehicle in this plane.

For purposes of comparison these instructions have been retained unchanged in subsequent years, although it appears that they could have been improved slightly. About one seventh of the students do not draw a plan, but instead produce an elevation or perspective drawing which is usually unintelligible, so it might have been better to provide a duplicated figure. The symbol R was proposed to minimise the amount of writing on the diagram, but this is probably a source of confusion to some students to whom R usually means reaction, whatever that signifies to them.

The problem should present no difficulty to anyone who understands the idea of acceleration and Newton's second law. The acceleration in this case is radially inward, hence the resultant force must also be in this direction. As there is no angular acceleration, R acts through the centre of mass. There are only two bodies with which the vehicle can interact, the road and the air. There is air resistance, which must be very nearly directly opposite in direction to the instantaneous velocity. The resultant force of friction exerted by the road, F, must combine vectorially with air resistance to give R. Hence F must be directed as shown in figure 14.

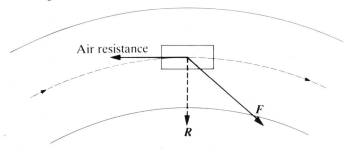

Figure 14 For our most widely used test the student is not given a duplicated diagram, but is asked to sketch a plan showing the resultant force R, the frictional force acting on the tyres, F, and any other horizontal force acting on a uniformly turning vehicle. Only four students out of several hundred tested have given a correct sketch (shown here).

When the problem was first set, in 1969, three students out of one hundred and forty-eight gave correct answers. Since then only one student has done so.

Of the students who give intelligible answers, 40% show R acting forwards, 28% radially inwards and 28% radially outwards. This in itself suggests that uniform circular motion is little understood. What is perhaps more significant, is that, in most cases, the arrow marked **R** is quite obviously not the resultant of the component forces shown. In 1969 one third of the intelligible diagrams showed **R** actually representing the resultant. (In most of these cases **R** was coincident with **F**, and no other forces were shown.) Subsequently the proportion of diagrams in which **R** was in fact the resultant fell rapidly, becoming one tenth after four years.

The resultant force of road friction, **F**, is shown acting backwards (40%), radially inwards (40%) or outwards (20%). The number of cases in which it has a forward component is negligible.

Air resistance is shown by 10% of students. Other forces shown are centrifugal (40%), centripetal (20%) and driving (25%). The latter two categories do not include those few students who recognise that components of **F** act in these directions. The classification is based on the directions shown rather than simply upon the label because, for example, outward forces are often called centripetal.

Students who have been taught to use imaginary forces to give zero resultant on any body might be expected to treat this problem differently from those taught Newtonian methods. We observe, however, that those who introduce a centrifugal force do not do so in a way consistent with the methods of Coriolis or d'Alembert.

Jets

A test which was tried with physics freshmen used a duplicated diagram showing a sprinkler, similar to figure 11. The students were asked to draw arrows to represent forces exerted by the water upon the sprinkler. The problem proved to be too difficult and most of the diagrams received were unintelligible, at least in part. The only consistent feature was that backward forces, usually called 'reaction', were commonly shown acting on the nozzles or upon space somewhere near them.

A simpler test was then given to a class of twenty-two first year physics students (Warren 1975). Each student was given a diagram of a

Figure 15 Diagram from a tutorial test. The student is asked to indicate the forces exerted by the water on the hose, which is shown in plan.

hose (similar to figure 15) and asked to show the forces exerted by the water.

Only two of the answers showed a force at the pipe caused by the water being deflected from vertical to horizontal motion, and one of these and one other showed outward forces acting at the bend. In sixteen answers a backward force was shown acting at the nozzle. In no case was a forward force shown on the nozzle.

6
Discussion

Problems

There is a controversy concerning the objectives of the teaching of elementary mechanics. The supposedly clearly defined aim of instilling the technique of solving problems is contrasted with the supposedly much vaguer aim of communicating understanding of the concepts. We may question whether this distinction has any real validity. It is doubtful whether any meaning can be given to the understanding of a scientific concept other than the mastery of its applications. If one can solve the relevant problems then one understands the concept. It is however necessary to consider precisely what this means.

A scientific problem usually has several components, with both qualitative and quantitative aspects. Qualitative considerations, such as those examined in the tests of Chapter 5, include recognition of the relevance of particular physical laws. Quantitative considerations include the ability to use the relevant formulae, competence in any necessary computation, knowledge of appropriate units and appreciation of accuracy.

Much of the difficulty which students have with the concept of force—and also with many other fundamental ideas of science—probably arises from a widespread misunderstanding of the nature and use of problems, both in teaching and in examining. A practical situation is too often regarded as a source of exercises in mathematics, rather than mathematics being regarded as an instrument helpful in the study of the situation. In consequence certain traditional types of 'problem' have been evolved which depend essentially on remembering a formula, doing a mathematical exercise (typically changing the subject of the formula) and putting in numerical values to obtain the answer. Now it is not argued that such procedures are not necessary. They are very necessary indeed, but they are not sufficient.

With practice even a relatively unintelligent student can learn to associate a radial force mv^2/r with uniform circular motion. If he has ordinary algebraic ability (or rather, what used to be regarded as ordinary ability) he can obtain the correct numerical answers to various stereotyped examples. He may, however, have no clear idea why there is such a force, upon what body it acts, where it acts, and in what sense it acts. His confusion is easily revealed by a suitably designed problem. According to one kind of test he knows the subject, according to another he does not.

Figure 16(a) shows one form of a diagram which, with slight variations, has appeared in several textbooks. The force of gravity on the cornering motorcyclist is combined with an imaginary centrifugal force

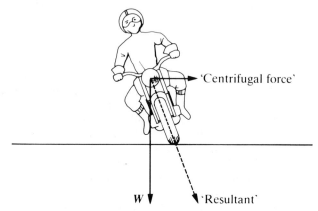

Figure 16 (a) Conventional misrepresentation of the forces acting on a cornering motorcyclist. The supposed resultant would, of course, accelerate the machine and rider into the earth.

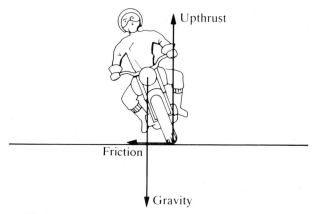

Figure 16 (b) Correct representation of the real forces acting on the motorcyclist in this plane. Their effect, which is to accelerate the cyclist to our left, would be produced by an equivalent single force acting through the centre of mass. This equivalent force is sometimes shown on diagrams as if it were an additional real force (marked 'centripetal'). Occasionally it is shown opposed by the imaginary 'centrifugal' force in diagrams that also include the real forces.

to give a supposed resultant, which, for no clearly stated reason, is required to act through the point where the wheels touch the ground. If this were really the resultant force the cyclist would, of course, accelerate into the ground. Now this very odd procedure does in fact give the right value for the angle at which the cyclist is leaning (or in a similar problem, the slope of the bank required to avoid lateral friction). If the sole purpose of an exercise were to obtain a particular numerical result such analyses could be regarded as correct. But the muddled ideas confuse the student who is consequently less able to follow futher developments of the subject. A correct treatment will, of course, give the right answer and also advance the students' appreciation of mechanics.

A teacher who has learnt an incorrect method may think that he understands it, and that it is easy, because frequent repetition has made it familiar to him and his own self-assurance convinces his students. He regards it as correct because it gives what is universally agreed to be the right answer. When he is told that the method is wrong and that he is confusing his pupils, he cannot comprehend the criticism. The effort of learning what is to him a new approach makes a sound treatment seem more difficult than the familiar unsound one. He does not see that, for a pupil who has not yet been taught any method, an approach using all the real forces and no imaginary ones, and correctly applying Newton's laws, will in fact be just as easy to memorise and infinitely more easy to understand than an unsound method. It is astonishing to find how many people believe that pupils 'understand' analyses which are, in fact, incoherent nonsense, simply because they can reproduce them on demand.

A generation ago many teachers of mechanics attempted to overcome the difficulties of teaching the rather abstract idea of mass by omitting the concept completely. The idea of weight was considered to be sufficiently concrete and unambiguous (!) to be understood easily and Newton's second law was taught in the form

$$\text{force/acceleration} = W/g$$

Students could be drilled in solving certain numerical questions using this equation and everything seemed superficially satisfactory. It was found, however, that the students had, in fact, acquired no understanding of dynamics and had increased difficulty in mastering more advanced ideas. They were gravely handicapped when studying those phenomena that do not depend on gravity, which, of course, constitute by far the greater number of those of interest in even elementary science and engineering. The author was one of many students who found it necessary to relearn the subject from first principles, this time including mass. When the W/g approach came under attack, defenders used the argument that their pupils could be taught to solve problems that way, so all was well. There was either something wrong with the problems, or with the way the answers were marked, or both.

We see that if a problem is to be useful in instructing students, or a suitable test of their competence, it must receive the correct *qualitative* treatment. There is little value in finding a 'correct' numerical answer without understanding what it means. Attention must be paid to quantitative aspects however. Too often questions are set with randomly chosen numerical data which often bear no relation to reality (Warren 1971(b)). It is also by no means unusual for a textbook to contain a worked example with data given to only one or two significant figures and the result given to four.

Precise and imprecise statements

A major cause of difficulty for students is the lack of precision in the statements of definitions and scientific laws. A definition should not be just a slogan to be memorised, but an exact description of something such that it can be recognised whenever it is encountered. Any law, even an approximate one, must be stated precisely, so that there is no doubt about what it means in any given circumstances.

Mechanics is concerned with predictable effects of known causes and cannot properly be expressed in terms of vague tendencies. Some elementary books 'define' force by saying that 'a force will cause a body to move, or tend to move'. It is hard to say which is worse, the bad physics (*move* instead of *accelerate*) or the absurd logic. Since 'tending to move' a body is contrasted with moving it, the statement above can only mean that a force is something which either moves a body or does not! One of the more striking features of the traditional absurd treatment of surface tension is the frequency with which it is said that under the supposed resultant force molecules will 'tend to move' into the interior.

One law of mechanics that is often expressed imprecisely is Newton's law of gravitation. In its correct form this states that every particle of matter in the universe attracts every other particle with a force given by

$$\text{force} = G\frac{m_1 m_2}{r^2}$$

where m_1 and m_2 are the masses of particles at a distance r apart and G is a universal constant. Particles are pieces of matter whose dimensions are infinitesimal compared with r, so there is no uncertainty in the magnitude of the distance or the direction of the force. To apply the law to extended bodies it is necessary to integrate.

It is very often taught that this law applies to the attraction of any bodies provided the distance is measured between the centres of mass.

It is instructive to apply this idea to the attraction of a particle placed a short distance away from a long straight thin rod. We could calculate the force by assuming that the mass of the rod is concentrated at the centre of mass. Alternatively we could regard the rod as being made of two halves and consider the mass of each half as being concentrated at its centre of mass, which would give a different value for the attraction. In fact we would obtain a different value for each way we chose to divide our specimen. Thus the law as it is commonly taught is meaningless since it does not give a definite result in every given case.

It is known that, although Newton's law of gravitation is very exact indeed, it must be replaced by an even more accurate law for the most refined astronomical calculations. This fact is sometimes proposed quite seriously as a justification for teaching it wrongly! It should be obvious that it is meaningless to discuss the accuracy or inaccuracy of any law unless it is stated in precise terms.

Language

It is becoming increasingly difficult to communicate with students because many technical words are no longer used consistently. Ambiguities in the use of *velocity, acceleration, weight, weightless* and *reaction* have already been discussed, but there are many more. Even such elementary mathematical expressions as *term* and *factor* are confused by some authors. Some mathematics teachers now give different meanings to *vector* and *function* from those more generally understood.

Many difficulties arise from abuse of the concept of proportionality. If $y = mx$, where m is a *constant*, then y is directly proportional to x. Proportionality is often incorrectly treated as being synonymous with the general rectilinear relationship expressed by $y = mx + c$, where c is a constant. Proportionality requires a straight line graph *through the origin* and it is misleading to say that a relationship is linear when one means that it is a proportionality, and it is wrong to say that it is a proportionality when it is only linear. It is not unknown for a textbook to illustrate experimental results by a graph with a straight line which does not pass through the origin, and yet to assert that the variables are proportional. Similar invalid assertions are made concerning rectilinear sections of curves that do not extrapolate through the origin. In such a case it may even be said that the ratio y/x is constant. Often the phrase 'proportional to' is used to mean just 'dependent on', and in some books it sometimes has one meaning and sometimes the other. Even more confusingly, a dependent variable is sometimes said to be proportional to two or more different variables. For example, the acceleration of a body may be said to be proportional to the applied force and inversely proportional to the mass. Such relationships can only properly be described by equations. If we have a dependent variable proportional to the product of a number of *independent* variables it is possible to derive various proportionalities to the separate variables, each of which applies in different circumstances, but we must be careful how we present this idea to students unless they have fully mastered partial differentiation.

Students are commonly taught to add vectors and the sum is conventionally called the resultant. But some writers change their convention when they add forces. It can happen that the resultant force acting on a body is called the effective force whilst, incredibly, one of the components may be called the resultant.

Those followers of d'Alembert who introduce the imaginary inertia force will say that an accelerated body is in 'dynamic equilibrium'. In their scheme every body is in either static or dynamic equilibrium, so the word equilibrium ceases to have any meaning.

The need for coherence

Even at the very lowest levels of thought there is a need for systematic rules. An infant learns that certain effects always follow certain causes. Later he masters more abstract general principles. Two and two are four, whether one is adding apples or stairs or pennies. As learning progresses he advances to more and more complex rules but the demand for system and consistency is an unchanging requirement. Nowhere is this more important than in the physical sciences. If we are to understand natural phenomena we must think coherently, whether our studies are directed towards practical applications, original discovery, intellectual training or aesthetic satisfaction.

Young people studying mechanics are far too often exposed to a bewildering mixture of rigidity and chaos. There is an appearance of structure in the course, with what purport to be definitions, principles and laws. Certain rules have (sometimes) to be obeyed punctiliously. Yet the 'rules' change in the most irrational way from one occasion to another. What is the effect of there being no force acting on a body? It appears that the body may be unaccelerated, or bouncing, or moving in a circle. What if there is a force? The body may move, or 'tend to move' or accelerate, or neither move nor accelerate but instead be stretched or sheared. A charge is expected to move along an electric line of force, but a planet or a tennis ball is not expected to move along a gravitational line of force (but see p.56).

It is very usual for different conventions to be adopted by different teachers. Thus the physics teacher may use Newton's laws, whilst the mathematics teacher uses inertia forces, or vice versa.

In the normal concerns of everyday life and in performing the duties of a citizen, persons without any scientific education are expected to think logically. A jury is required to listen to evidence about the most complicated occurrences and to determine the truth. This demands that the ordinary citizen, who often has only had an elementary education, must exercise a much higher capacity for logical thought than is commonly exhibited by many university graduates who teach or write books on mechanics. The innate ability of the scholar has been gravely diminished by studying and working in accordance with a degraded intellectual tradition.

Conclusion

The idea of force is of very great importance in elementary science, engineering and mathematics. It is obviously very widely misunderstood, not only by students, but also by highly qualified, mature adults. It is very hard to assess how intrinsically difficult the idea is, since it has been made very much more difficult in practice by the almost incredible confusion of approach, which has continued unchecked by any action by any professional body. Paradoxically, if we were generally to recognise that it is difficult and were to teach it accordingly, the subject would become more easy.

Vectors and pseudovectors

The word vector is used with different meanings by different scholars. Some mathematicians use the term to describe *any* quantity which can be expressed as a row or column matrix. It is more usual for physicists, engineers and also many mathematicians to limit it to those quantities which have magnitude and direction in real space. A further distinction which is of importance in some applications is that between *true vectors* (polar vectors) and *pseudovectors* (axial vectors).

True vectors are those that can be regarded as occurring or acting in a direction. Displacement, velocity, acceleration, momentum and force are all true vectors. Their dimensions include length to the first power, or more rarely to other odd powers. They are odd functions, that is, if the directions of a set of Cartesian co-ordinates are reversed, the components of a vector parallel to the axes change their signs.

Pseudovectors involve the orientation of an axis in space. Their dimensions may exclude length (e.g. angular velocity) or include it squared or to other even powers (e.g. torque and angular momentum). They are even functions, that is their components do not change sign when the co-ordinates are reversed.

Both vectors and pseudovectors add according to the polygon rule and multiply to form *dot products* (inner or scalar products) or *cross products* (outer or vector products).

Any product of two polar vectors or product of two pseudovectors must be an even function. In both cases the inner product is a scalar, and the outer product a pseudovector. For example, the inner product of the two true vectors, force and displacement, is a scalar, work; their outer product is a pseudovector, torque.

The area of a plane surface can be regarded as the cross product of two vectors and is therefore a pseudovector, the axis being a normal to the surface. We can find a dot product of the area times a third displacement, giving a volume. The latter might at first appear to be a scalar; but as it is the product of an odd function and an even one, it must therefore be an odd function. It is called a *pseudoscalar*.

Pseudoscalars have magnitude but not direction. Their dimensions include length to an odd power. Two examples are density and the constant, G, in Newton's law of gravitation. Fluid pressure P is also a pseudoscalar. This is most simply defined as the normal force F divided by area S, but as we cannot directly divide such quantities it is conventional to formulate it as

$$P = \frac{F \cdot S}{S^2}$$

The dimensions of P include reciprocal length.

The terms of an equation must all be of the same form: scalar, pseudoscalar, vector or pseudovector. (We shall not consider more complex tensors). For example, consider Bernoulli's equation

$$P_1 - P_2 = \tfrac{1}{2} \rho \, (v_2^2 - v_1^2)$$

The square of velocity is a scalar. Density is a pseudoscalar, so the right hand side is a pseudoscalar, as is the left.

These ideas can be applied to electromagnetism. Charge is a scalar, so current (charge/time) is a scalar; current density (current/area) is a pseudovector; and charge density (charge/volume) is a pseudoscalar. The electric field intensity E (force divided by charge) is a vector. By Coulomb's law the permittivity ε is a pseudoscalar, so electric displacement D ($= \varepsilon E$) is a pseudovector.

Similarly the magnetising field H is a vector, permeability μ is a pseudoscalar, and induction B is a pseudovector.

When a positive charge q moves with velocity v in a magnetic field of induction B, it is acted on by a force F given by

$$F = (v \times B)q$$

The outer product of a vector and a pseudovector is a vector, the directions being related by the right-hand rule of vector multiplication. If one extends the first two fingers and thumb of the right hand, the first finger points in the direction of the first factor v, the second finger represents the second factor B, and the thumb then gives the direction of the product, which acts at right angles to the plane containing the factors (a negative charge moving in the opposite direction experiences the same force).

This law is commonly presented in the equivalent form given by Fleming's left-hand rule, in which B is represented by the first finger and v by the second finger of the left hand. The rule is often expressed in a misleading way, the first and second fingers being said to represent flux and current respectively. But as we have already seen, current is a scalar—as is flux, which is the inner product of induction and area.

Similar errors are frequently made in stating Fleming's right-hand rule for the induced field in a body cutting lines of induction. Here the first finger should be said to represent B and not flux; the second finger represents the velocity of the body, and the thumb represents the direction of the resultant electric field in the body. The latter is usually said to represent either induced e.m.f. or current, neither of which is a vector. The term 'flux lines' used in both electricity and magnetism is incorrect.

Tension and surface tension

It is probable that much of the difficulty found in understanding the molecular cause of surface tension arises from the fact that the more basic problem of explaining tension in a solid is generally ignored.

To account for the stability of matter we assume that molecules interact by short-range forces that are repulsive at very close distances and attractive at slightly larger separations, with the attractive forces rising to a maximum and then falling off to zero very rapidly, as shown for a pair of molecules in figure 17(a). (See also Appendix 3.) Figure 17(b) shows the corresponding potential energy variation for either molecule. The curves in (a) and (b) are related since force equals minus the gradient of potential energy. The equilibrium separation of an isolated pair of molecules is r_0, where the potential energy gradient is zero.

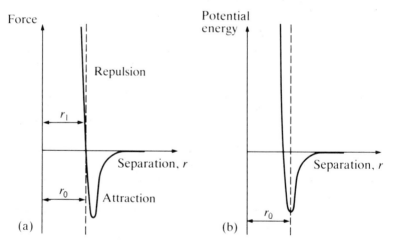

Figure 17 Variation of force and potential energy with separation for the interaction of an isolated pair of molecules.

Molecules are never at rest and oscillate rapidly (with frequencies typically of the order of 10^{12} Hz) about equilibrium points which in solids remain fixed, and in liquids move very slowly compared with the speeds of oscillation.

For simplicity consider a one-dimensional structure in the form of a row of molecules, shown in their equilibrium positions in figure 18. Except for a small variation near the ends of the row these 'lattice

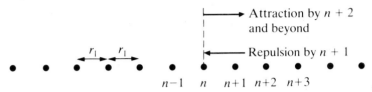

Figure 18 The interactions within a hypothetical isolated unstressed row of molecules.

points' are equally spaced with a separation r_1 that is slightly less than r_0. Each molecule is repelled by its nearest neighbours on each side, but attracted by more distant molecules. On considering any small displacement of a molecule in the line of the structure in relation to figure 17(a), we see that the resultant forces will act towards the undisplaced position, thus giving a stable oscillating system. (Bending of the row is assumed to be excluded; in real bodies it is prevented by the molecules' interactions with molecules outside the row).

If the body is unstressed the resultant force exerted by one part upon the other averages to zero over a time that is large compared with the period of oscillations. If attractive forces are applied to each end of the row by outside bodies the molecules move slightly further apart. Now the molecules to the right of number n are, on balance, attracted by those up to and including n. From 17(a) we see that the row can resist tension up to a limiting value. Similarly it can resist compression to an unlimited amount.

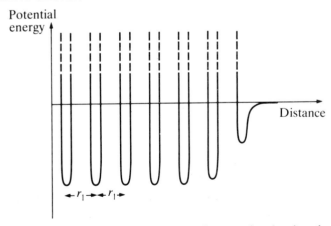

Figure 19 Potential wells for part of a row of molecules; the shallower wells on the right are those for end molecules.

Appendix 2

The potential energy of a molecule at any point in the row, except near the ends, is approximately twice that resulting from interaction with one near neighbour at separation close to r_0. This is because there are two near neighbours at distances r_1 which are not very different from r_0, and the contribution of the more distant molecules is small, as is apparent from figure 17(b). The particles oscillate in potential wells as shown in figure 19. The end molecules are in wells of roughly half the depth of the others because they each have only one near neighbour.

Any real condensed material is three dimensional and is therefore more complex than the structure described above, but the general argument still applies. Molecules in the surface layer are in potential wells that are significantly less deep than those in the interior. Hence there is 'surface energy' in both solids and liquids. Molecules in a liquid are free to adjust their positions, and in a steady state there will be a lower density of molecules in the surface than in the interior. In the plane of the surface, molecules are separated by large enough distances for the resultant force on either side to be attractive—that is there is tension.

Long-range and short-range forces

Interactions between bodies can be divided into two classes according to the form of the relationship between force and distance. Whatever the law may be when the bodies are very close, in all cases the forces

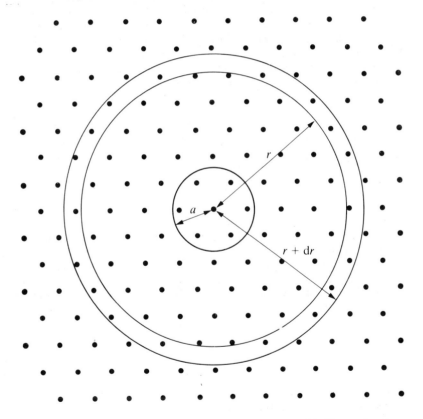

Figure 20 Intermolecular interactions in a solid or liquid. The molecule shown at the centre repels its neighbours within the sphere of radius a, and attracts all those at greater distances. The number of molecules between r and $r + dr$ is assumed to be proportional to the volume element.

decrease with distance when the separation of the bodies increases beyond a certain point. Long-range interactions, such as gravitation, fall off only slowly with distance and it is obvious that the forces act 'through space'. Some interactions, such as intermolecular ones, fall off very rapidly with distance and it is usual to say that they act 'when the bodies are in contact', which is really a tautology. A very naïve distinction is often made between these classes; and long-range forces are regarded as mysterious, whilst the more complex short-range ones are taken for granted. Conversely the Cartesian superstition that matter is absolutely impenetrable (used by d'Alembert) leads to the idea that the effects of short-range interactions occur without there being any forces.

The significance of 'range' in this context can be illustrated by a simple example. Consider the potential energy of a molecule inside a solid or liquid (figure 20). The interaction between any two molecules will follow a law as illustrated in figure 17. Beyond a distance a rather larger than r_0 the force is attractive and decreases with distance. Let us assume that this can be represented to sufficient accuracy by an inverse power law, that is for r greater than a, we have

$$\text{force} \propto \frac{1}{r^n}$$

whence the potential energy of one molecule because of the presence of the other is given by

$$\text{potential energy} \propto -\frac{1}{r^{n-1}}$$

The total potential energy of the molecule shown in figure 20 results from its interactions with all the other molecules surrounding it. The near neighbours up to distance a give energy U_0, and to find the contribution of the more distant molecules we consider those in the shell between r and $r + dr$. The number of these is assumed to be proportional to the volume element $4\pi r^2 dr$, whence the potential energy becomes

$$U = U_0 - A \int_a^b \frac{dr}{r^{n-3}}$$

where A is a constant and b represents a limit determined by the dimensions of the material.

Consider two cases:

(1) $n \leqslant 4$. The value of the integral increases indefinitely with the size of the specimen, tending to infinity as b tends to infinity. This

is the case of long-range forces. Stars are held together by gravitational forces in this way and their properties depend upon size.

(2) $n > 4$. The value of the integral at the upper limit tends to zero as b tends to infinity, so the magnitude is determined by the lower limit, which represents the molecule's interactions with its near neighbours. This is the case of short-range forces.

The properties of matter on the scale of everyday objects are practically independent of scale. For example the specific latent heats of evaporation of liquids and sublimation of solids are the same whatever the sizes of the specimens. This shows that the molecular interactions are effectively short-range.

If we wished to examine all materials in detail we should, of course, have to consider various complications to the simple argument given above. For example, interactions within ionic materials involve both attraction and repulsion of distant particles according to the inverse-square law. In this case we should have to consider the variation with distance of the net charge in the elementary shell, which would give effectively a short-range interaction.

One interesting application of these ideas is to atomic nuclei. The mean binding energy per nucleon, which is roughly proportional to the potential energy, is approximately constant over a wide range of nuclear sizes. This shows that the principal interactions (by charge-independent nuclear forces) are short-range. The repulsive electric forces between protons are long-range and therefore become proportionally more significant for larger nuclei. This leads to the highly significant facts that the proportion of neutrons is higher in large nuclei and that fission of very large nuclei releases energy.

In all the above arguments it has been tacitly assumed that the particles can be located fairly precisely in space. A simple application of Heisenberg's indeterminacy relation shows that this is sufficiently true for our purpose for molecules and nucleons. Because of their small mass, electrons cannot be located precisely; hence we have no reason to believe that there are any short-range repulsive forces in an atom preventing electrons collapsing into the nucleus.

Tides

It is widely known that tides are caused by the gravitational pull of the moon upon the sea, but that is about all that most people ever learn about the subject. Many people believe that there is only one high tide a day, whilst those students who know better find the facts mysterious. They will say 'I understand why there is a bulge in the sea on the same side as the moon, but not why there is one on the other side.' Of course, if they really understood why one bulge appears, they would also understand the reason for the other. What is commonly ignored is the fact that the moon attracts the earth as well as the sea, and that it is the *difference* between the two forces which matters.

Consider two astronomical bodies P and Q which can be regarded as very nearly spherically symmetrical (figure 21). The distance between their centres is R and the radius of P (the body in which we are studying the tides) is r.

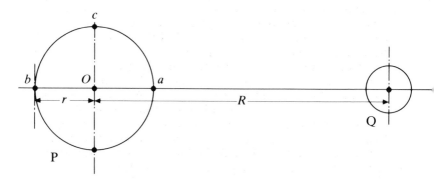

Figure 21 Diagram to illustrate the production of tide-generating forces at various points at the surface of the planet P by the moon or sun at Q.

The average force exerted by Q upon any unit mass of matter in P is equal to the value of the force at the centre O, which is given by

$$A_O = \frac{GM_Q}{R^2}$$

where M_Q is the mass of Q, and G is Newton's constant.

Unit mass at the point a is subject to the attraction

$$A_a = \frac{GM_Q}{(R - r)^2} = A_O\left(1 + \frac{2r}{R}\right)$$

where we have expanded by the binomial theorem and assumed that r^2 is negligible compared with R^2.

Thus we see that unit mass at a is attracted to Q by a force that differs from the average by an amount $2A_O r/R$ radially outwards. We can call this a tide-generating force.

Similarly, at b we have

$$A_b = A_O\left(1 - \frac{2r}{R}\right)$$

so here there is a tide-generating force of equal magnitude which also acts radially outwards since A_b is less than A_O.

The force on unit mass at c can be resolved into a component parallel to the line joining the centres of P and Q, which is equal to A_O (to the degree of approximation assumed), and a component towards O, which is equal to $A_O r/R$. Thus we can say that at c, and at the point diametrically opposite to c, there are tide-generating forces acting inwards.

Because the forces differ around the circumference, the otherwise spherical body P is slightly distorted, with bulges at a and b. Rotation or orbital motion will cause the bulges to move round the surface, producing tides. At intermediate points the tide-generating forces are not radial and strictly it is their horizontal components which cause the ebb and flow. Because of inertia, friction and local disturbances there is normally a time lag, so the high tides occur some time after Q has passed directly overhead or underfoot.

Our tides are caused jointly by the sun and the moon. The lunar generating forces are more than twice the solar forces and, as the tidal range varies more than proportionally to the forces, the moon causes roughly six times the effect of the sun. Because the orbital motion of the moon is in the same sense as the axial rotation of the earth, there are intervals of roughly twelve and a half hours between successive high tides. By itself the sun would cause high tides every twelve hours. In effect it causes a periodic variation in the amplitude of the tides. It is easily seen that the maximum tide-generating forces occur when the moon, earth and sun are in line at the full moon and new moon, giving the maximum amplitude a day or two later (spring tides). Similarly the minimum amplitude (neap tides) follow the first and last quarters.

A useful article on this subject is given in the *Encyclopaedia Britannica*.

Significant quotations

The difficulties that students meet can be illustrated by considering selected passages from textbooks.

> . . .Statics, the study of forces on bodies at rest . . . . Dynamics, the study of the motion of a body together with the forces which cause the motion.
>
> (Murphy 1971)

Correctly, statics is the study of bodies in equilibrium, that is bodies that are unaccelerated, and dynamics is the study of forces that cause *changes* of motion. The mistaken idea that rest is natural and that motion has to be caused is implicit in much elementary teaching.

> A body, of mass m kg, is placed on a horizontal plane which is moving with an upward vertical acceleration a m s^{-2}. Find the reaction between the body and the plane.
>
> Let R N be the reaction between the body and the plane. Since the body is moving upwards with an acceleration, it is evident that R is greater than the weight mg. . .
>
> If the plane be moving downwards with acceleration a, the weight mg is now. greater than R. . .
>
> (Humphrey and Topping 1971)

Here we have confusion between motion and acceleration. It is totally irrelevant whether the plane is moving upwards or downwards or is instantaneously at rest; the only thing that matters is the way the acceleration is directed. Note also the confusion of the meaning of symbols, which are first used to represent numbers and then to represent physical quantities. This is very common.

> Experience tells us that all objects fall vertically downwards, in other words the earths' gravitational force is directed towards the centre of the earth.
>
> (Schools Council 1974)

The statement as it stands is preposterous, but presumably it means that objects dropped from 'rest' fall vertically in the absence of disturbance. Experience over the past three hundred years has in fact shown that bodies fall to the east of the vertical as defined by a plumbline. An observer who was not rotating with the earth would find that the falling body follows the arc of an ellipse with the centre of the earth at the more distant focus. It is, however, less important to consider the technical inaccuracy of the passage than the implicit assumption about

forces. Clearly the reader is expected to believe that bodies move in the
direction of the applied force.

> Force produces or tends to produce movement in a body. If we push against
> a brick wall, we do not produce movement. . . . If we push with a bulldozer, of
> course, we shall produce movement!
>
> (Hay and Hughes 1972)

Notice, in this extract, the idea of force causing motion or 'tending' to
do so. One thing that has been overlooked is the fact that when one
pushes against a wall opposing forces are usually applied through the
soil. Only if the system is stressed until the base of the wall breaks is
there a resultant force on the wall.

> The applied force tries to overcome the resistance to movement. It is less
> than the resistance to movement. Note: the resistance to movement is a
> *reaction force* and equals but never exceeds the applied force.
>
> (Timings 1973)

Here the idea of the 'reaction' acting on the same body as the 'action'
appears explicitly. This same idea is expressed in the following extracts
(the first two are statements of the third law):

> To every action there is an equal but opposite reaction required to obtain
> equilibrium.
>
> (Douglas and Crichton 1972)

> If a body is stationary or moving with constant velocity then any applied
> force must have an equal and opposite force.
>
> (Lovelace 1970)

> When two forces are in equilibrium they must be equal, opposite and
> collinear. Proof of this principle is embodied in Newton's third law. . .
>
> (Jenson and Chenoweth 1972)

These examples illustrate confusion betweeen Newton's first and third
laws. The latter authors also extend the idea to the imaginary inertia
force:

> In the first and second of Newton's laws, mention is made of an unbalanced
> force, which must be external, but the third law states that to every action
> there is an equal and opposed reaction. This would suggest that the reaction
> to the unbalanced external force or action might be an internal force or
> reaction, which could only be the inertia of the body. . .

This analysis misses the essential point that the third law refers to
forces acting on different bodies. Thus the real force on another body is
omitted from the argument and the imaginary inertia force (here
confused with inertia itself) is introduced as if it were a real force
resulting from Newton's third law. Internal forces properly mean
forces exerted by one part of a body on another part, but here they are
supposed to act on the body as a whole.

On a later page we learn that in uniform circular motion there is

> [a] constant accelerating force . . . called the centripetal force. Its equal and opposed reaction (Newton's third law), which must be an inertia force, is called the centrifugal force.

The continuously changing centripetal force is said to be constant and the third law is misapplied.

The subjects above are treated with interesting variations by another author (Walker 1972) under the heading 'Inertial [sic] forces and d'Alembert's Principle'.

> Newton's third law of motion states that to every action there is always an equal and opposite reaction. A force applied to a mass with the purpose of accelerating it is referred to as the accelerating force. Immediately this is applied, an equal and opposite internal force, known as an inertial force, is produced in the mass, and this force makes the mass resist any change of motion.

It is very hard to understand the last phrase. The inertia force is purely imaginary and does not 'resist' anything. The change of motion occurs whether we invent any such 'forces' or not, and the invented force is given a magnitude equal to the rate of change of momentum. That is, if it successfully resisted the change of motion it would have zero value!

The same author later discusses circular motion of a mass at the end of a string:

> But while the string is pulling the mass towards the centre, it is also true that there is an equal and opposite reaction on your hand at the centre. This opposite reaction is known as the centrifugal force. It is equal in magnitude to the centripetal force, and exists only as an equal and opposite reaction to this centripetal force. It is an example of the inertial force which was discussed along with d'Alembert's principle.

The force acting on the hand is, of course, a perfectly real force and has nothing whatever to do with any ficticious one. In the first passage quoted the author has made it clear that his 'inertial force' is supposed to act on the body concerned, but in the second one it is supposed to act on another body.

The simple problem of a body resting on a table causes much trouble:

> Since the body is in contact with the table, the weight W_1 of the body is being balanced by an equal and opposite reaction force of the table on the body.
>
> (Murphy 1971)

It is hard to interpret this. The reference to forces being 'balanced' implies the first law, whence we conclude that weight means the force of gravity on the body. But 'reaction' invokes the third law, which suggests that weight means the force exerted by the body on the table, in which case it appears that forces on different bodies are supposed to balance. Elsewhere this author uses the third law correctly, and usually uses weight to mean the force exerted on a support; but he also states:

> If we imagine a body to be falling freely, the only force on the body is its own weight.

This analysis could result in a student misunderstanding the third law. The difficulty probably originates from ambiguity in the meaning of weight. A different 'definition', which also leaves doubt about where weight acts, is given in the following:

> Weight is the natural downward force due to the mass of an object.
>
> (Lovelace 1970)

In some accounts of jet propulsion, a force is explicitly said to act on the wrong body:

> The reaction force on a nozzle . . . may be used to propel the nozzle and the craft to which it may be attached.
>
> (Massey 1970)

Failure to consider all the bodies involved in an interaction is illustrated by the following description of the recoil of a gun:

> If the gun is free to move in the direction of the barrel the forward momentum generated in the shot at the instant it leaves the barrel is equal to the backward momentum generated in the gun.
>
> (Humphrey and Topping 1971)

The gun also expels a large mass of gas generated by the explosion of the propellant and hence the recoil momentum is usually substantially greater. It is even possible to produce a gun that does not recoil, by designing it so that a large proportion of the gas is expelled backwards.

The confused use of the concept of proportionality is shown by:

> Force of gravity . . . is proportional to the masses of the bodies, inversely proportional to the distance between them. . .
>
> (Douglas and Crichton 1972)

(Note also the reference to 'bodies' rather than to particles.)

The seriousness of the confusion now prevailing in the use of this very elementary mathematical principle is shown by a discussion of the electrical analogue of forced vibrations. An incorrect circuit is used, with inductor and capacitor in parallel, the combination being in series with a signal generator and a resistor of high value. To measure the current a CRO is connected across the inductor:

> The CRO records the p.d. across the inductance, giving a measure of the current flowing through it. The frequencies are the same and the amplitudes are directly proportional, but there is a difference in phase.
>
> (Schools Council 1974)

Appendix 5

The current would, of course, only be proportional to the p.d. if the impedance were constant. As the frequency changes, so does the impedance, making nonsense of the analysis.

References

Douglas, I. J. and Crichton, J. D. G. 1972. *Engineering Mechanics.*
Edinburgh: Oliver and Boyd
Den Hartog, J. P. 1948. *Mechanics.* New York: McGraw-Hill
Elton, L. R. B. 1971. *Concepts of Classical Mechanics.* Maidenhead:
McGraw-Hill
Hay, G. A. and Hughes, D. 1972. *First-year Physics for Radiographers.*
London: Baillière Tindall
Humphrey, D. and Topping, J. 1971. *Intermediate Mechanics, vol. 1:
Dynamics.* S. I. edn. London: Longman
Jensen, A. and Chenoweth, H. H. 1972. *Applied Engineering Mechanics.* 3rd
edn. New York: McGraw-Hill
Lovelace, T. A. 1970. *Engineering Principles.* London: Nelson
Mach, E. 1919. *The Science of Mechanics*, trans. T. J. McCormack. 4th edn.
Chicago: Open Court Publishing Company
Massey, B. S. 1970. *Mechanics of Fluids.* 2nd edn. London: Van Nostrand
Reinhold Company
Murphy, P. 1971. *Applied Mathematics Made Simple.* London: W. H. Allen
Schools Council/Loughborough University of Technology. 1974–5. *Schools
Council Engineering Science Project.* London and Basingstoke: Macmil-
lan Education Ltd
Timings, R. L. 1973. *Basic Engineering.* London: Longman
Verne, J. 1865. *De la Terre à la Lune*
Walker, J. D. 1972. *Applied Mechanics.* 4th edn. London: English Univer-
sities Press
Warren, J. W. 1965. *The Teaching of Physics.* London: Butterworths

Warren, J. W. 1971a. 'Circular motion'. *Physics Education,* vol. 6, p. 74
1971b. 'Thinking quantitatively'. *Physics Education,* vol. 6, p. 238
1975. 'Forces acting on a hose'. *Physics Education,* vol. 9, p. 327

Index

Index